EXERCISES IN ESSENTIAL ARITHMETIC

Book 3

EXERCISES IN ESSENTIAL ARITHMETIC

Book 3

E. BUCKLEY
Deputy Headmaster
(formerly head of Mathematics Department)
Hollin High School
Middleton, Manchester

A. GRAY
Head of Mathematics Department
Hollin High School
Middleton, Manchester

A Division of Pergamon Press

A. Wheaton & Company Limited
A Division of Pergamon Press
Hennock Road, Exeter EX2 8RP

Pergamon Press Ltd
Headington Hill Hall, Oxford OX3 0BW

Pergamon Press Inc.
Maxwell House, Fairview Park, Elmsford, New York 10523

Pergamon of Canada Ltd
Suite 104, 150 Consumers Road,
Willowdale, Ontario M2J 1P9

Pergamon Press (Australia) Pty Ltd
P.O. Box 544, Potts Point, N.S.W. 2011

Pergamon Press GmbH
6242 Kronberg/Taunus, Pferdstrasse 1,
Frankfurt-am-Main, Federal Republic of Germany

First published 1980

Printed in Great Britain by A. Wheaton & Co. Ltd, Exeter (T.S.)

ISBN 0 08 024167 0

Foreword

Exercises in Essential Arithmetic Books 1, 2 and 3 offer a course of basic minimum arithmetic and have been designed to allow much needed practice for the purpose of ensuring that necessary processes are understood and skills acquired.

Some of the more difficult concepts treated have not been completed in any one particular book. Rather, they have been structured to be dealt with at different times on a progressive basis involving recapitulation at each stage.

Multiplication Square

×	1	2	3	4	5	6	7	8	9	10
1	1	2	3	4	5	6	7	8	9	10
2	2	4	6	8	10	12	14	16	18	20
3	3	6	9	12	15	18	21	24	27	30
4	4	8	12	16	20	24	28	32	36	40
5	5	10	15	20	25	30	35	40	45	50
6	6	12	18	24	30	36	42	48	54	60
7	7	14	21	28	35	42	49	56	63	70
8	8	16	24	32	40	48	56	64	72	80
9	9	18	27	36	45	54	63	72	81	90
10	10	20	30	40	50	60	70	80	90	100

Number

PLACE VALUE

1. Consider the number 760:

    (a) What is the value of the 6?   **(b)** What is the value of the 7?

2. Consider the number 1005:

    (a) What is the value of the 1?   **(b)** What is the value of the 5?

3. Consider the number 28 600:

    (a) What is the value of the 8?   **(b)** What is the value of the 2?

4. Consider the number 40 032:

    (a) What is the value of the 4?   **(b)** What is the value of the 3?

5. Consider the number 672 345:

    (a) What is the value of the 6?   **(b)** What is the value of the 2?

6. Consider the number 800 052:

    (a) What is the value of the 2?   **(b)** What is the value of the 8?

7. Consider the number 907 080:

    (a) What is the value of the 7?   **(b)** What is the value of the 8?

8. Consider the number 7 005 012:

    (a) What is the value of the 7?   **(b)** What is the value of the 5?

9. Consider the number 23 053 700:

    (a) What is the value of the 5?   **(b)** What is the value of the 2?

10. Consider the number 246 005 003:

    (a) What is the value of the 2?   **(b)** What is the value of the 4?

WRITING NUMBERS

Write the following in figures:

1. (a) Eight hundred and fifty-four
   (b) Two hundred and ninety
   (c) Seven hundred and one

2. (a) Five thousand
   (b) Six thousand, two hundred and fourteen
   (c) Eight thousand, nine hundred

3. (a) Two thousand, three hundred and four
   (b) Three thousand and thirty-three
   (c) Nine thousand and five

4. (a) Fifteen thousand
   (b) Twenty-three thousand, five hundred and eleven
   (c) Seventy-four thousand, seven hundred

5. (a) Fifty thousand and fifty
   (b) Sixty-two thousand, two hundred and four
   (c) Eighty thousand and eight

6. (a) Two hundred thousand
   (b) One hundred and forty-two thousand, one hundred and twelve
   (c) Five hundred and sixty thousand, four hundred

7. (a) Four hundred thousand, seven hundred
   (b) Five hundred and twenty thousand and twenty-five
   (c) Six hundred thousand and six

8. (a) Seven million
   (b) Four million, eight hundred thousand, eight hundred
   (c) Three million, three thousand and three

9. (a) Sixteen million, three hundred and twenty-five thousand
   (b) Forty million, seven hundred and ten
   (c) Seventy million, seven hundred thousand

10. (a) Two hundred and thirty-four million, eight thousand and fifty
    (b) Five hundred and two million, seventy thousand, three hundred
    (c) One hundred million and one

ADDITION

1. (a) 342
   + 123
   _____

   (b) 123
   40
   + 116
   _____

   (c) 6
   11
   + 402
   _____

2. (a) 503 + 46   **(b)** 3 + 42 + 250
   (c) What is the sum of the following?
   12, 303, 21, 2, 640

3. (a) 247 + 719   **(b)** 101 + 29 + 317
   (c) Find the total of the following:
   36, 204, 9, 117, 520

4. (a) 4 + 39 + 275   **(b)** 359 + 84 + 136
   (c) 86 plus 729 plus 154

5. (a) 749 + 358 + 19   **(b)** 905 + 398 + 47
   (c) If 543 is increased by 279 and then by a further 84, what will be
   the result?

6. (a) 1000 + 2143   **(b)** 2140 + 1207 + 6400
   (c) Add three thousand, one hundred and forty to two thousand,
   eight hundred and five.

7. (a) 2431 + 12 + 204   **(b)** 4 + 12 + 110 + 2001
   (c) Find the total of two hundred and seventy-two; twenty-four;
   three thousand; four hundred and one.

8. (a) 2486 + 3734   **(b)** 1089 + 2405 + 3870
   (c) Four thousand, eight hundred and ninety-six + 707 + one
   thousand, one hundred and ten.

9. (a) 98 + 247 + 5900   **(b)** 89 + 175 + 4862 + 649
   (c) The mileage of a car is 6887 km. What will it be after a journey
   of 258 km?

10. (a) 9857 + 4756   **(b)** 3000 + 8755 + 275
   (c) The attendance at a cup-tie which resulted in a draw was
   8652 and at the replay which brought a result it was 9768. What
   was the total attendance?

E.I.E.A. BK. 3—*

11. (a)
```
    10000
      147
+   3202
_____
```

(b)
```
       22
    22341
+    1625
_____
```

(c)
```
    21400
        7
+    2001
_____
```

12. (a) 33486 + 20017   **(b)** 40788 + 4296
  (c) What is the sum of the following: 168, 23015, 9, 17, 5000?

13. (a) 14285 + 498 + 700   **(b)** 870 + 48675 + 7005
  (c) Find the total of the following: 7228, 855, 26430, 8, 48.

14. (a) 89472 + 36 + 1724   **(b)** 65045 + 3425 + 1530
  (c) 54785 plus 38 plus 8592 plus 146

15. (a) 54728 + 900 + 47064   **(b)** 32075 + 23 + 69386
  (c) If 84336 is increased by 7845 and then by 16080, what will be
     the result?

16. (a) 130211 + 42325   **(b)** 202374 + 40400
  (c) Add two hundred and thirty-six thousand to thirteen thousand
     and forty.

17. (a) 146374 + 2408   **(b)** 23798 + 586312
  (c) Find the total of four hundred and eighty-six thousand, three
     hundred and seventy-nine and twenty-three thousand and
     sixty-five.

18. (a) 748234 + 29076   **(b)** 49655 + 378575
  (c) Eight hundred and forty-two thousand + 876 + fifty-nine
     thousand, six hundred and fifty-four.

19. (a) 824065 + 500000   **(b)** 900000 + 803103
  (c) A firm makes an annual profit of £824000. If it plans to exceed
     this profit by three-quarters of a million pounds next year,
     what profit can be expected?

20. (a) 745629 + 761278   **(b)** 453468 + 546532
  (c) In July 845629 copies of a monthly magazine were sold and
     758426 were sold in August. How many were sold during
     these two months?

21. (a)   1 432 125   **(b)**   3 426 050   **(c)**   146
                  2 013   300 700   7 324 000
       +   300 201   +   11 020   +   10 720
       _____   _____   _____

22. (a) 3 517 352 + 2 069   **(b)** 8 279 000 + 148 120
   (c) Find the sum of the following: 7 000 550, 375 800, 6 250.

23. (a) 708 906 + 6 345 846   **(b)** 7 986 275 + 154 725
   (c) Find the total of the following: 848 255, 1078, 8 575 890.

24. (a) 4 547 219 + 3 452 781   **(b)** 8 584 397 + 6 340 706
   (c) 3 217 425 plus 4 802 505 plus 5 091 180.

25. (a) 10 800 400 + 76 200   **(b)** 94 376 847 + 5 623 153
   (c) If 95 million is increased by 6 750 895 and then by 375 725,
       what will be the result?

Rewrite these additions, replacing the asterisks with the correct figure:

26. (a) *4   **(b)** 6*   **(c)**   1*
        5*   *8   1*7
        __   __   ___
        71   95   *23

27. (a) 13*   **(b)** 3*8   **(c)** *7*
        2*6   25*   2*9
        ___   ___   ___
        *94   *82   788

28. (a) *6*   **(b)** 4*6   **(c)** 57*
        1*4   29*   **6
        ___   ___   ___
        551   *84   961

29. (a) 1487   **(b)** 2*6   **(c)** 580*
        6**   3*4*   **74
        ____   ____   ____
        **00   *224   77*0

30. (a) 1*437   **(b)** 134 56*   **(c)**   34***46
        82**   ***99   **0437*
        ____   _____   _____
        *0*00   *046*7   11 2729*5

SUBTRACTION

1. (a)
$$57 - 34$$

(b)
$$75 - 50$$

(c)
$$89 - 39$$

2. (a) $40 - 7$ **(b)** $54 - 29$
(c) What must be added to 18 to make 63?

3. (a) $154 - 44$ **(b)** $860 - 420$
(c) How much more than 350 is 965?

4. (a) $291 - 47$ **(b)** $582 - 354$
(c) What is the result of subtracting 175 from 792?

5. (a) $500 - 91$ **(b)** $800 - 753$
(c) Subtract six hundred and seventy-eight from nine hundred.

6. (a) $724 - 589$ **(b)** $311 - 199$
(c) What will be the result if 803 is reduced by 234?

7. (a) $5492 - 402$ **(b)** $6748 - 2340$
(c) A car purchased for £7480 is later sold for £6350. Work out its loss in value.

8. (a) $7347 - 588$ **(b)** $9003 - 7171$
(c) Eight thousand, two hundred and four minus five thousand, two hundred and sixty-six.

9. (a) $6000 - 485$ **(b)** $8000 - 1699$
(c) A journey of 9000 km is to be covered in two stages. The first stage is 6375 km. What distance is the second stage?

10. (a) $7400 - 2550$ **(b)** $6130 - 3485$
(c) Which number is 4480 fewer than 8400?

11. (a)   19 650
     − 8 220
     ─────

(b)   12 780
     −   560
     ─────

(c)   23 476
     − 2 455
     ─────

12. (a) $35\,690 - 24\,530$ **(b)** $63\,180 - 41\,070$
    (c) The attendance at a cup-tie was 49 480 compared with the attendance for a league match between the same two teams of 37 350. How many more persons attended the cup-tie?

13. (a) $16\,244 - 8556$ **(b)** $34\,015 - 25\,119$
    (c) If 47 235 is reduced by 17 346 what will be the result?

14. (a) $10\,000 - 755$ **(b)** $25\,000 - 2425$
    (c) Subtract three thousand, four hundred and fifty-six from twelve thousand.

15. (a) $45\,400 - 75$ **(b)** $38\,050 - 960$
    (c) Which number is 434 less than 27 800?

16. (a) $50\,250 - 7364$ **(b)** $40\,095 - 23\,299$
    (c) What must be added to 19 244 to make 33 830?

17. (a) $95\,264 - 47\,365$ **(b)** $51\,251 - 23\,484$
    (c) 43 255 copies of a local newspaper are sold one week and 52 130 copies the following week. Work out the increase in sales.

18. (a) $163\,630 - 31\,410$ **(b)** $750\,648 - 220\,412$
    (c) An engineering union has 346 682 members and 121 570 vote in favour of accepting a pay award. How many members were not in favour of accepting the award if all voted?

19. (a) $342\,502 - 153\,470$ **(b)** $676\,890 - 286\,903$
    (c) 636 400 minus 307 501

20. (a) $100\,000 - 6266$ **(b)** $250\,000 - 117\,077$
    (c) How much more than 73 375 is 320 000?

21. (a) 1 959 000   **(b)**   2 468 000   **(c)**   9 480 568
     −   336 000   − 1 455 000   − 3 240 165
     —————————   —————————   —————————

22. (a) 1 313 000 − 754 000   **(b)** 4 023 085 − 1 440 706
(c) What must be added to 2 506 714 to make 7 232 008?

23. (a) 3 000 000 − 37   **(b)** 6 400 000 − 1898
(c) Reduce two million by five hundred and sixty.

24. (a) 28 000 000 − 7 160 500   **(b)** 73 500 000 − 21 224 000
(c) Subtract 17 500 600 from thirty-nine million.

25. (a) 83 000 000 − 6 500 000   **(b)** 47 400 000 − 23 350 000
(c) The population of a country increases from 38 660 000 to 43 300 000 over a period of time. Work out the increase in population.

Rewrite the following subtractions, replacing the asterisks with the correct figure.

26. (a) 46   **(b)** 6*   **(c)** *1
       **   48   4*
       ——   ——   ——
       24   *5   49

27. (a) 26*   **(b)** *2*   **(c)** ***
       *2   83   95
       ——   ——   ——
       *12   *7   262

28. (a) 736   **(b)** *0*   **(c)** *22
       ***   253   6**
       ——   ——   ——
       497   2*2   189

29. (a) **0*   **(b)** 24*0   **(c)** 3***
       5*5   *5*   824
       ——   ——   ——
       463   *448   *249

30. (a) 2*0*   **(b)** *0*3   **(c)** ***4
       *0*9   3*3*   2575
       ——   ——   ——
       1009   788   498*

MULTIPLICATION

1. (a) 30
      × 2
_____

(b) 45
      × 2
_____

(c) 36
      × 3
_____

2. (a) 48×5 **(b)** 56×7
    (c) What is 79 multiplied by 8?

3. (a) 212×3 **(b)** 340×2
    (c) What is 102 times 4?

4. (a) 127×4 **(b)** 168×7
    (c) Multiply the product of 35 and 8 by 3.

5. (a) 505×5 **(b)** 808×6
    (c) What is the result of multiplying six hundred and six by nine?

6. (a) 3110×3 **(b)** 4108×2
    (c) What is the result of multiplying two thousand, one hundred and seventy-nine by four?

7. (a) 43×10 **(b)** 37×20
    (c) If the result of multiplying 18 by 25 is 450, what is 18 times 50?

8. (a) 24×12 **(b)** 44×11
    (c) If the result of multiplying 16 by 26 is 416, what is 32 times 13?

9. (a) 58×27 **(b)** 67×59
    (c) A clothing firm produces 90 suits per week. How many will be produced in 46 working weeks?

10. (a) 231×23 **(b)** 327×15
    (c) 435 employees received a Christmas bonus of £31 each. What was the total bonus issued?

11. (a)   307   **(b)**   490   **(c)**   586
$$\begin{array}{r} 307 \\ \times\ \ 64 \\ \hline \end{array} \qquad \begin{array}{r} 490 \\ \times\ \ 53 \\ \hline \end{array} \qquad \begin{array}{r} 586 \\ \times\ \ 45 \\ \hline \end{array}$$

12. (a) 3485×5 **(b)** 7408×9
    (c) What is 5864 multiplied by 7?

13. (a) 4525×10 **(b)** 3075×50
    (c) What is 20 times 7406?

14. (a) 2132×33 **(b)** 4025×15
    (c) Multiply the product of 40 and 80 by 27

15. (a) 5106×45 **(b)** 3007×56
    (c) What is the result of multiplying two thousand, four hundred and eighty by sixty-three?

16. (a) 21302×3 **(b)** 30514×5
    (c) What is the result of multiplying twenty-five thousand, seven hundred and fifty by six?

17. (a) 212000×4 **(b)** 375050×7
    (c) If the result of multiplying 250575 by 8 is 2004600, what is 250575 times 4?

18. (a) 63500×10 **(b)** 23102×30
    (c) If the result of multiplying 14220 by 2 is 28440, what is 1422 times 20?

19. (a) 13200×23 **(b)** 24525×15
    (c) 15850 articles are produced per day by a machine which operates continuously. How many will be produced in a fortnight?

20. (a) 36213×55 **(b)** 28005×37
    (c) The average attendance for the 45 matches played by a first division club during a season was 35050. What was the aggregate attendance for the season?

21. (a)   525
          × 100
          _____

(b)   214
      × 200
      _____

(c)   303
      × 300
      _____

22. (a) 123 × 123   **(b)** 230 × 230
    (c) What is 100 multiplied by itself?

23. (a) 237 × 128   **(b)** 256 × 145
    (c) What is 178 times 275?

24. (a) 700 × 700   **(b)** 846 × 235
    (c) Multiply the product of 20 and 25 by the product of 25 and 30.

25. (a) 1023 × 300   **(b)** 2306 × 500
    (c) What is the result of multiplying one thousand, eight hundred and ninety by six hundred?

26. (a) 2013 × 313   **(b)** 3005 × 142
    (c) What is the result of multiplying four thousand and six by one hundred and twenty-five?

27. (a) 4832 × 820   **(b)** 5806 × 725
    (c) If the result of multiplying 4921 by 900 is 4 428 900, what is 4921 times 450?

28. (a) 12 310 × 132   **(b)** 42 500 × 600
    (c) If the result of multiplying 54 720 by 3 is 164 160, what is 54 720 times 300?

29. (a) 146 782 × 22   **(b)** 234 500 × 50
    (c) The approximate speed of light is 298 000 km/s. How far would light travel in half a minute?

30. (a) 345 000 × 100   **(b)** 345 000 × 300
    (c) What is the product of a quarter of a million and a half of a thousand?

DIVISION

1. (a) $2\overline{)48}$ (b) $3\overline{)69}$ (c) $4\overline{)88}$

2. (a) $75 \div 3$ (b) $75 \div 5$
   (c) If the dividend is 96 and the divisor is 6 what will be the quotient?

3. (a) $480 \div 4$ (b) $780 \div 6$
   (c) What will be the result of dividing nine hundred and fifty by five?

4. (a) $287 \div 7$ (b) $568 \div 8$
   (c) Divide six hundred and thirty-nine by nine.

5. (a) $576 \div 4$ (b) $738 \div 6$
   (c) Work out 945 divided by 5.

6. (a) $8064 \div 2$ (b) $5490 \div 3$
   (c) What is the value of one eighth of 9680?

7. (a) $4350 \div 5$ (b) $9128 \div 8$
   (c) A car covers 5130 km in 9 days. Work out the average distance covered each day.

8. (a) $1956 \div 2$ (b) $8575 \div 7$
   (c) If 5552 is split into 8 equal parts what will be the value of each part?

9. (a) $5340 \div 6$ (b) $5970 \div 3$
   (c) A milkman delivers 5250 bottles of milk in 7 days. How many bottles per day does this represent?

10. (a) $8000 \div 4$ (b) $6300 \div 7$
    (c) 7200 articles are pre-packed in cartons of 8 in readiness for sale at a supermarket. How many cartons will there be?

11. (a) $3\overline{)9609}$ **(b)** $4\overline{)5224}$ **(c)** $7\overline{)9135}$

12. (a) $6184 \div 2$ **(b)** $8328 \div 4$
    (c) Divide five thousand, three hundred and fifty-five by five.

13. (a) $4242 \div 6$ **(b)** $5640 \div 8$
    (c) A small bakery produces 6328 loaves in 7 working days. How many loaves per day does this figure represent?

14. (a) $6027 \div 3$ **(b)** $9081 \div 9$
    (c) 6048 is divided into six equal parts. What is the value of each part?

15. (a) $5990 \div 10$ **(b)** $7870 \div 10$
    (c) What is the value of one tenth of eight thousand, five hundred and sixty?

16. (a) $4550 \div 50$ **(b)** $2580 \div 60$
    (c) How many times is twenty contained in 3780?

17. (a) $90\,690 \div 3$ **(b)** $95\,045 \div 5$
    (c) How many times is six contained in seventy-two thousand and eighteen?

18. (a) $293\,216 \div 4$ **(b)** $400\,728 \div 8$
    (c) If 531 009 is divided by 3 and the resulting number also divided by 3 what will be the final result?

19. (a) $720 \div 12$ **(b)** $910 \div 13$
    (c) In a warehouse 840 cases are stacked in piles of 14. How many piles will there be?

20. (a) $3600 \div 15$ **(b)** $6400 \div 16$
    (c) If 18 persons share equally a syndicate win of £9000 what will be the amount each person receives?

21. (a) $19\overline{)9500}$ **(b)** $8\overline{)96\,000}$ **(c)** $22\overline{)88\,000}$

22. (a) $600\,000 \div 8$ **(b)** $740\,000 \div 37$
   (c) How many times is twelve contained in four hundred and eighty thousand?

23. (a) $2\,000\,000 \div 5$ **(b)** $4\,500\,000 \div 15$
   (c) Divide three million by six.

24. (a) $6851 \div 17$ **(b)** $52\,078 \div 26$
   (c) 50 075 is divided by one quarter of a hundred. What is the result?

25. (a) $80\,060 \div 20$ **(b)** $160\,120 \div 40$
   (c) 150 150 is split into fifty equal parts. How many in each?

26. (a) $4\,804\,800 \div 24$ **(b)** $4\,500\,900 \div 45$
   (c) A factory produces 8 405 600 items during the 28 days of February. How many items per day does this represent?

27. (a) $96\,900 \div 30$ **(b)** $23\,450 \div 50$
   (c) How many hours are there in 50 280 minutes?

28. (a) $45\,318 \div 14$ **(b)** $73\,024 \div 16$
   (c) A garage purchases 15 new cars of the same make and design at a total cost of £72 525. Work out the cost of each car.

29. (a) $80\,532 \div 36$ **(b)** $910\,360 \div 44$
   (c) What is the value of 173 208 divided by 42?

30. (a) $4\,205\,406 \div 58$ **(b)** $13\,068\,144 \div 72$
   (c) A company makes a profit of £18 840 848 in a year. How much profit does this represent per week?

PROBLEMS

1. 1274 people were present at a concert. If 185 were children, how many were adults?

2. An engineering company has 14 branches, each having a full quota of 850 employees. How many people are employed by the company?

3. The amounts received from 6 areas within a region as the result of an appeal to help handicapped people were £3842, £5408, £2104, £988, £1095 and £872. What was the total amount received in the region?

4. How many minutes are there in 12 720 seconds?

5. A college library has a total stock of half a million books. If 12 872 were out on loan, how many books were in the library?

6. A pools syndicate of 9 people won dividends totalling £2574. How much did each person receive?

7. A newspaper's sales for six consecutive weekdays were 814 262, 796 511, 809 205, 799 850, 804 958 and 810 876. What were the total sales for the week?

8. An entertainer is offered a contract of £16 500 for a series of three TV shows each lasting 50 minutes. How much income per minute does this contract represent?

9. Of ten million newly minted coins 7 750 000 are put into immediate circulation. How many are retained?

10. If there are 15 chocolates in a box and 10 boxes make up a carton, how many chocolates would be required to fill 30 cartons?

11. The official attendance figures for the 5 days of a test cricket match were 22 458, 17 184, 31 095, 21 908 and 8804. What was the total number of spectators at the match?

12. 18 528 cars passed a census point during a 24-hour period. What was the average number of cars passing the point per hour?

13. What is the area of a square which has a perimeter of 800 m?

14. A person wins a first dividend of £558 400 on the football pools. How much more than half a million pounds is this?

15. Multiply the sum of 346 and 328 by their difference.

16. A cathedral launched a restoration fund and its aim was to reach one million pounds in three years. After two years the amount raised was £628 496. How much short of the target was this?

17. An air route measures 4582 km. What distance does an aircraft cover on this route if it makes 122 journeys during the year?

18. Divide the sum of 2052 and 948 by the product of 75 and 40.

19. A man withdrew £200 from the bank in new five-pound notes numbered consecutively. If the first note was numbered 714 584, what was the number of the last note?

20. A number is divided by 4 and then 78 is added to the result giving a total of 100. What is the number?

Perimeter, Area and Volume

Perimeter of rectangle = 2(length + breadth)
Area of rectangle = length × breadth
Area of triangle = $\frac{1}{2}$(base × height)
Volume of prism = area of cross-section × height

RECTANGLES AND TRIANGLES

In the table below, each question gives some information about either a square or a rectangle. Copy and complete the table.

	length	breadth	perimeter	area
1.	1 m	1 m		
2.	5 cm	4 cm		
3.	10 mm	8 mm		
4.	50 m	10 m		
5.	27 mm	13 mm		
6.	45 mm	45 mm		
7.	2 m	$\frac{1}{2}$ m		
8.	$3\frac{1}{2}$ cm	2 cm		
9.	5.4 m	2.6 m		
10.	17.8 cm	12.5 cm		
11.	2 m		6 m	
12.		3 cm	20 cm	
13.	$7\frac{1}{2}$ m		20 m	
14.		2.5 m	21 m	
15.		8 cm		120 cm²
16.	60 mm			1200 mm²
17.		$\frac{3}{4}$ km		3 km²
18.		0.8 km		1.6 km²
19.		6.4 m	32.9 m	
20.		2.2 cm		17.16 cm²

21. Find:
    (a) the perimeter
    (b) the area

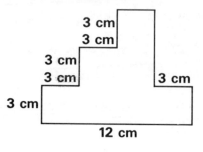

22. Find:
    (a) the perimeter
    (b) the area

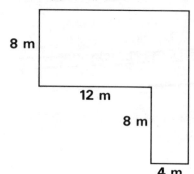

23. Find the area

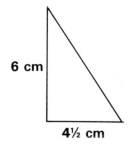

24. Find the area

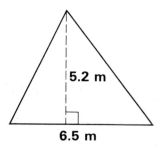

25. The perimeter of a square is 24 cm. Calculate its area.

26. Calculate the perimeter of a square if its area is 49 cm².

27. The perimeter of a rectangle is 40 m and its breadth is 4 m. Calculate the area.

28. A rectangle has a length of 4.8 m and breadth 3.2 m. Calculate **(a)** the perimeter, **(b)** the area.

29. The area of a triangle is 18 m². If its base is 12 m, what is its perpendicular height?

30. The base of a triangle is twice its perpendicular height. If its area is 9 m², find the base.

PRISMS

1. Find:
  (a) the total surface area
  (b) the volume

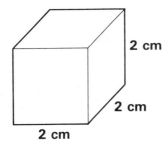

2 cm
2 cm
2 cm

2. Find:
  (a) the total surface area
  (b) the volume

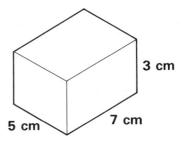

3 cm
5 cm
7 cm

3. Find:
  (a) the total surface area
  (b) the volume

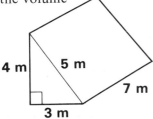

4 m
5 m
7 m
3 m

4. Find the volume

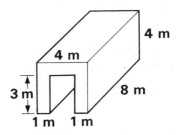

4 m
4 m
3 m
8 m
1 m   1 m

5. Calculate **(a)** the total surface area, **(b)** the volume of a 5 cm cube.

6. Calculate **(a)** the total surface area, **(b)** the volume of a rectangular prism with dimensions 4 cm, 6 cm and 10 cm.

7. How many cubes of edge 1 cm can fit into a hollow cube of edge **(a)** 2 cm, **(b)** 10 cm?

8. How many cubes of edge 2 cm can fit into a hollow cube of edge 4 cm?

9. How many cubes of edge 3 cm can fit into a hollow cube of edge 9 cm?

10. The volume of a triangular prism is 1000 m³. If the cross-sectional area is 50 m², what is its length?

E.I.E.A. Bk. 3—***

In the table below each question gives some information about a rectangular prism. Copy and complete the table. All measurements are in metres.

	length (m)	breadth (m)	depth (m)	surface area (m²)	volume (m³)
11.	1	1	1		
12.	4	3	2		
13.	10	9	7		
14.	15	12	10		
15.	$4\frac{1}{2}$	4	6		
16.	5	$2\frac{1}{2}$	1		
17.	$\frac{1}{2}$	$\frac{1}{2}$	$\frac{1}{2}$		
18.	5.2	4	3		
19.	8	4	2.5		
20.	4.4	1	3.5		
21.	2	2			8
22.	3		1		6
23.		5	4		160
24.	10		10		1000
25.		10	10		2000
26.	8	5			1200
27.		1	$\frac{1}{2}$		1
28.	5	1.4			21
29.		4	4	96	
30.	5	5		150	

PROBLEMS

1. A brick has dimensions 22 cm, 11 cm and 7 cm. What is its volume?

2. What is the volume of a school gymnasium 25 m long, 12 m broad and 8 m high?

3. In the previous question, what is the total area of the walls?

4. A rectangular box has a length of 10 cm and a width of 5 cm. What depth would be required if it was to hold 200 cm^3?

5.

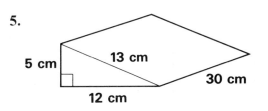

The diagram shows a triangular prism. Calculate **(a)** the volume, **(b)** the total surface area.

6. A rectangular lawn 15 m long and 8 m wide is completely surrounded by a flower-bed 1 m wide. What is the total area of the garden?

7.

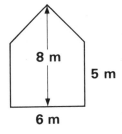

The diagram shows the gable-end of a house. What would a builder charge for pointing it if his price was £3 per square metre?

8. How many cubes with edge 10 mm will be required to make a cube of edge 10 cm?

9. How many cubes of edge 5 cm can be fitted inside a cubic metre?

10. How many of the bricks in Question 1 would be in a rectangular stack measuring 22 m by 11 m by 7 m?

27

11. How many boxes 20 cm long, 16 cm broad and 20 cm deep can be fitted inside a cubic container of edge 80 cm?

12. A woodwork room has a perimeter of 30 m. If it is twice as long as it is wide, what is its area?

13. The perimeter of a square is 3.6 m. Calculate its area in square metres.

14. The total surface area of a cube is 150 cm². What is its volume?

15. A rectangular fish tank has dimensions 1 m, 40 cm and 50 cm. Calculate **(a)** the volume of the tank in cubic metres, **(b)** the number of litres of water in the tank when it is $\frac{3}{4}$ full. (1 litre = 1000 cm³)

16. A room is 4.8 m long, 4.2 m broad and 3 m high. If its walls are to be painted with emulsion, how much paint will be required if 1 litre will cover 12 m²?

17. What area of metal would be required to make an open rectangular water tank with length 1 m, width 0.5 m and depth 0.75 m?

18. A piece of wood in the form of a triangular prism is 1 m long and has a volume of 4000 cm³. If the base of the cross-section is 8 cm, what is the perpendicular height of the cross-section?

19. The base of a rectangular tropical fish tank has a length of 80 cm. If its volume is 128 000 cm³ and the height is the same as the breadth, what is the breadth?

20.

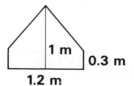

1 m

0.3 m

1.2 m

The diagram shows the cross-section of a tent which has a volume of 1.56 m³. What will be the area of the groundsheet?

Decimals

ADDITION AND SUBTRACTION

1. (a)   14.8   **(b)**   135.5   **(c)**   746.9
        + 21.7   + 76.5   + 205.1

2. (a)   27.5   **(b)**   137.3   **(c)**   430.2
        − 14.2   − 84.5   − 170.5

3. (a) 23.04 + 12.05 + 0.75
   (b) 120.5 + 79.37 + 1.74
   (c) 756.4 + 0.75 + 78.39

4. (a) 17.34 − 11.02
   (b) 146.73 − 78.9
   (c) 358.06 − 109.3

5. (a) 27.4 + 15 + 35.6 + 11
   (b) 8 + 0.95 + 1.7 + 3.06
   (c) 0.07 + 1.08 + 5 + 18.2

6. (a) 24.95 − 16
   (b) 20 − 9.1
   (c) 73 − 59.24

7. (a) 146.7 + 100 + 379.85 + 86.08
   (b) 350.2 + 1001.5 + 73.75
   (c) 2029.8 + 3500 + 680.9 + 215.25

8. (a) 39.24 − 16.77
   (b) 85.6 − 29.49
   (c) 113.1 − 78.54

9. (a) 0.026 + 0.737 + 0.507
   (b) 0.986 + 0.44 + 0.7
   (c) 0.347 + 0.1 + 0.22 + 0.333

10. (a) 0.704 − 0.32
    (b) 0.83 − 0.555
    (c) 0.1 − 0.023

11. (a) Find the sum of 5.235, 4.38 and 0.009
  (b) Find the total of 3.07, 11, 24.266 and 6.058
  (c) Find the aggregate of 123.895, 236.055 and 79.83

12. (a) From 6.034 subtract 2.78
  (b) Subtract 17.345 from 47.342
  (c) How much more is 8 than 0.625?

13. (a) Add 6380.4, 364.39, 97.08 and 6.266
  (b) Find the aggregate of 672.87, 1000, 19.443 and 770
  (c) 13 782 plus 829.78 plus 75.375

14. (a) From 2.1 subtract 0.363
  (b) By how much does 36.42 exceed 1.084?
  (c) How much is 10 000 in excess of 3704.275?

15. (a) 36.024 + 117.8 − 94.057
  (b) 720 − 259.8 + 100.24
  (c) 1000 − 17.34 − 24.86

16. (a) 67.245 plus 112 minus 42.048
  (b) 337.8 minus 18.46 plus 105.625
  (c) 1 minus 0.003 minus 0.107

17. (a) Add 4.86 to 13.09 then subtract 5.007
  (b) Subtract 89 from 108.24 then add 17.065
  (c) From 700 subtract 137.86 then subtract 50.624

18. (a) From the sum of 18.274 and 1.859 subtract 11.027
  (b) Subtract 136.52 from the sum of 200 and 187.4
  (c) From 5000 subtract the sum of 36.288 and 17.094

19. (a) 783.4 less the sum of 18.79 and 46.725
  (b) By how much is 820 greater than the sum of 59.86 and 7?
  (c) From the sum of 1.304 and 0.88 subtract the sum of 0.008 and 0.563

20. From a full five-litre jar of acid a chemist pours 0.34 litres, 0.225 litres and 0.07 litres into separate flasks. How much acid remains in the jar?

MULTIPLICATION AND DIVISION

1. (a) 0.2×4 (b) 1.2×3 (c) 0.4×5
2. (a) 25.2×3 (b) 0.02×4 (c) 0.09×5
3. (a) 1.48×6 (b) 3.29×9 (c) 17.58×4
4. (a) 23.85×7 (b) 124.3×7 (c) 208.8×8
5. (a) 0.001×5 (b) 0.009×9 (c) 0.024×4
6. (a) 0.037×6 (b) 0.056×10 (c) 0.073×50
7. (a) 0.562×8 (b) 2.375×4 (c) 3.886×7
8. (a) 4.728×10 (b) 7.114×30 (c) 8.219×60
9. (a) 12.012×3 (b) 56.459×4 (c) 123.82×8
10. (a) 51.829×10 (b) 12.025×13 (c) 254.07×45
11. (a) 4.77×100 (b) 0.395×100 (c) 49.009×200
12. (a) 0.075×1000 (b) 4.86×1000 (c) 0.8×4000
13. (a) 0.1×0.1 (b) 0.8×0.9 (c) 3.7×0.6
14. (a) 0.7×4.5 (b) 8.2×0.7 (c) 1.5×1.5
15. (a) 7.6×4.2 (b) 3.8×9.1 (c) 6.9×6.9
16. (a) 42.7×0.3 (b) 4.4×40.9 (c) 115.5×3.6
17. (a) 0.3×0.02 (b) 0.08×0.5 (c) 0.75×0.8
18. (a) 4.27×0.6 (b) 33.49×2.4 (c) 215.5×8.7
19. (a) 12.2×1.41 (b) 52.1×2.46 (c) 5.21×24.6
20. (a) 27.34×42.8 (b) 163.5×8.68 (c) 372.85×26.1
21. (a) $6.5 \div 5$ (b) $4.2 \div 7$ (c) $37.8 \div 3$
22. (a) $0.08 \div 4$ (b) $0.78 \div 6$ (c) $3.24 \div 4$
23. (a) $17.84 \div 8$ (b) $35.63 \div 7$ (c) $28.04 \div 10$
24. (a) $0.7 \div 2$ (b) $15 \div 4$ (c) $76 \div 8$
25. (a) $0.009 \div 3$ (b) $0.096 \div 6$ (c) $0.056 \div 7$
26. (a) $0.84 \div 8$ (b) $0.198 \div 9$ (c) $0.763 \div 7$
27. (a) $4.212 \div 6$ (b) $25.616 \div 8$ (c) $111.006 \div 9$
28. (a) $52.54 \div 20$ (b) $6.25 \div 50$ (c) $62.4 \div 100$
29. (a) $365 \div 100$ (b) $5204 \div 1000$ (c) $28259 \div 1000$
30. (a) $0.7 \div 100$ (b) $9 \div 1000$ (c) $1486277 \div 1000$

31. (a) $1 \div 0.1$ (b) $96 \div 0.4$ (c) $480 \div 0.5$

32. (a) $0.9 \div 0.3$ (b) $7.2 \div 0.9$ (c) $17.2 \div 0.4$

33. (a) $3 \div 0.4$ (b) $0.81 \div 0.6$ (c) $1.02 \div 0.5$

34. (a) $0.006 \div 0.2$ (b) $7.056 \div 0.7$ (c) $18.738 \div 0.9$

35. (a) $72 \div 1.2$ (b) $3.9 \div 1.3$ (c) $0.56 \div 1.4$

36. (a) $400 \div 2.5$ (b) $64.16 \div 3.2$ (c) $0.018 \div 4.5$

37. (a) $9 \div 0.03$ (b) $1.7 \div 0.04$ (c) $0.025 \div 0.05$

38. (a) $0.007 \div 0.14$ (b) $140.7 \div 0.35$ (c) $75.075 \div 0.75$

39. (a) $234.5 \div 0.08$ (b) $23.45 \div 0.08$ (c) $105 \div 0.24$

40. (a) $0.09 \div 0.002$ (b) $6.3 \div 0.009$ (c) $800 \div 0.025$

41. (a) $\dfrac{2}{0.005}$ (b) $\dfrac{0.147}{0.007}$ (c) $\dfrac{84}{0.012}$

42. (a) $\dfrac{0.06}{0.015}$ (b) $\dfrac{1.32}{0.022}$ (c) $\dfrac{2.626}{0.052}$

43. (a) $0.2 \times 0.2 \times 0.2$ (b) $1.5 \times 1.5 \times 1.5$
(c) Find the product 1.59, 0.8 and 3

44. (a) $\dfrac{3.14 \times 2.6}{0.13}$ (b) $\dfrac{0.7 \times 0.7}{0.001}$

45. (a) $\dfrac{22.5}{0.45 \times 20}$ (b) $\dfrac{1.75}{2.5 \times 1.4}$

46. (a) $\dfrac{3 \times 4}{0.3 \times 0.4}$ (b) $\dfrac{0.42 \times 0.4}{80 \times 0.07}$

47. Divide the product of 1.6 and 2.5 by 0.032

48. Divide 0.84 by the product of 0.7 and 0.03

49. Divide the sum of 4.725 and 1.275 by the product of 120 and 50

50. The volume of a rectangular prism is $4.2 \, \text{m}^3$. If the length is 3.5 m and width 2.4 m, find the height.

PROBLEMS

1. Four packing-cases prepared for export weigh 3.48 tonnes, 4.725 tonnes, 5.25 tonnes and 2.15 tonnes. What is the total mass of the export order?

2. A bridge has headroom of 6.2 m. A removal van 5.38 m high is to pass under the bridge. Calculate the excess headroom.

3. A river ferry is carrying 5 cars weighing 1.275 tonnes, 0.95 tonnes, 1.45 tonnes, 0.985 tonnes and 1.36 tonnes. What is the combined mass of the cars?

4. 0.26 litres of acid is poured from a jar which contains 1.5 litres. How much acid is left in the jar?

5. In two minutes a shop till registers the following amounts: £1.75, 93p, 74p, £3.90, 8p, £2.44, £1.39 and £5.50. Calculate the total amount registered during this time.

6. How many plastic cups each holding 0.15 litres can be filled from a supply of 30 litres of orange juice?

7. At a football ground amounts of £1489.20, £1801.60, £1606.80, £2168.40, £2455.20 and £492.75 were collected from six turnstiles. What was the 'gate' money for this game?

8. What was the price per metre if 3.5 m of cloth cost £9.80?

9. A car travels 11.25 km on 1 litre of petrol. How far would it travel on 8.5 litres?

10. If the area of a rectangle is 25.5 cm^2 and the breadth is 3.4 cm, find the length.

11. A man has £217.84 in his current account and settles by cheque a gas bill for £74.82, an electricity bill for £32.79 and a telephone account for £21.36. How much money has he now left in his current account?

12. 15.575 g, 6.48 g and 7.325 g of a chemical are measured from a full 100 g packet. What mass of the chemical remains in the packet?

13. Calculate the cost of 8.5 m of material at £4.88 per metre.

14. The following lengths are cut from a metre length of copper wire: 8.4 cm, 7.2 cm, and 11.5 cm. How many centimetres remain?

15. A bowler takes 68 wickets in a cricket season at an average cost of 11.25 runs per wicket. What was the total number of runs he conceded in taking the wickets?

16. Stakes are placed at intervals of 1.5 m along the edges of a rectangular allotment 18 m long and 12 m broad. How many stakes are used?

17. A car can travel 10.8 km on 1 litre of petrol. How far will it travel on a full tank of 27.25 litres?

18. The sum of 5 numbers is 14.15. If 3 of these numbers total 7.3, what is the average of the other two numbers?

19. If the exchange rate between the English pound and American dollar is £1 = 1.98 dollars, how many dollars would be worth £26.50?

20. 100 units of a unit trust are purchased when the price is 45.9p per unit and later sold for a collective sum of £63.60. Calculate the profit made per unit.

Fractions

EQUIVALENCE

Complete the missing part of the fraction:

1. (a) $\frac{1}{2} = \frac{}{10}$ **(b)** $\frac{3}{4} = \frac{6}{}$ **(c)** $\frac{8}{} = \frac{1}{3}$

2. (a) $\frac{}{9} = \frac{6}{27}$ **(b)** $\frac{15}{} = \frac{3}{4}$ **(c)** $\frac{6}{5} = \frac{42}{}$

3. (a) $\frac{33}{36} = \frac{}{12}$ **(b)** $\frac{16}{25} = \frac{}{100}$ **(c)** $\frac{36}{} = \frac{9}{10}$

Write the following fractions in their lowest terms:

4. (a) $\frac{15}{30}$ **(b)** $\frac{9}{12}$ **(c)** $\frac{28}{35}$

5. (a) $3\frac{20}{24}$ **(b)** $\frac{76}{100}$ **(c)** $2\frac{35}{60}$

6. (a) $\frac{155}{500}$ **(b)** $\frac{240}{400}$ **(c)** $1\frac{225}{1000}$

Change the following mixed numbers to improper fractions:

7. (a) $4\frac{1}{3}$ **(b)** $5\frac{3}{4}$ **(c)** $3\frac{7}{8}$

8. (a) $6\frac{7}{10}$ **(b)** $7\frac{7}{9}$ **(c)** $10\frac{5}{6}$

9. (a) $4\frac{17}{20}$ **(b)** $3\frac{29}{50}$ **(c)** $3\frac{17}{100}$

Change the following improper fractions to mixed numbers:

10. (a) $\frac{7}{4}$ **(b)** $\frac{14}{3}$ **(c)** $\frac{19}{5}$

11. (a) $\frac{22}{7}$ **(b)** $\frac{39}{8}$ **(c)** $\frac{87}{10}$

12. (a) $\frac{47}{12}$ **(b)** $\frac{177}{50}$ **(c)** $\frac{289}{100}$

Change the following decimals to fractions in their lowest terms:

13. (a) 0.9   **(b)** 0.8   **(c)** 1.5

14. (a) 0.09   **(b)** 0.25   **(c)** 2.36

15. (a) 0.009   **(b)** 3.075   **(c)** 4.125

16. (a) 1.305   **(b)** 0.444   **(c)** 0.064

Change the following fractions to decimals:

17. (a) $\frac{7}{10}$ **(b)** $2\frac{1}{2}$ **(c)** $4\frac{2}{5}$

18. (a) $\frac{5}{4}$ **(b)** $\frac{3}{8}$ **(c)** $1\frac{7}{8}$

19. (a) $\frac{17}{20}$ **(b)** $\frac{49}{50}$ **(c)** $\frac{237}{100}$

20. (a) $\frac{2}{3}$ **(b)** $\frac{5}{6}$ **(c)** $2\frac{1}{6}$

ADDITION AND SUBTRACTION

1. (a) $\frac{1}{5} + \frac{3}{5}$ **(b)** $\frac{5}{16} + \frac{11}{16}$ **(c)** $\frac{2}{3} + \frac{2}{3} + \frac{2}{3}$

2. (a) $\frac{7}{10} + \frac{1}{10}$ **(b)** $\frac{3}{4} + \frac{3}{4} + \frac{3}{4}$ **(c)** $\frac{5}{12} + \frac{11}{12}$

3. (a) $\frac{7}{8} + 8$ **(b)** $2\frac{1}{6} + \frac{5}{6}$ **(c)** $3\frac{4}{5} + 4\frac{2}{5}$

4. (a) $\frac{1}{2} + \frac{1}{8}$ **(b)** $\frac{1}{2} + \frac{1}{3}$ **(c)** $\frac{1}{4} + \frac{1}{6}$

5. (a) $\frac{1}{3} + \frac{5}{9}$ **(b)** $1\frac{2}{3} + \frac{3}{5}$ **(c)** $5\frac{7}{8} + 6\frac{11}{12}$

6. (a) $\frac{5}{6} + 3\frac{2}{3}$ **(b)** $7\frac{9}{10} + 8\frac{4}{5}$ **(c)** $11\frac{3}{4} + 12\frac{11}{12}$

7. (a) $\frac{1}{3} + \frac{1}{12} + \frac{1}{6}$ **(b)** $\frac{3}{4} + \frac{4}{5} + \frac{17}{20}$ **(c)** $\frac{17}{18} + \frac{5}{6} + \frac{2}{3}$

8. (a) $\frac{1}{2} + \frac{2}{3} + \frac{3}{4}$ **(b)** $1\frac{2}{3} + 2\frac{3}{4} + \frac{4}{5}$ **(c)** $5\frac{1}{4} + \frac{11}{20} + 8\frac{3}{5}$

9. (a) $7 + 8\frac{7}{8} + 7\frac{5}{6}$ **(b)** $12\frac{11}{20} + 13 + 14\frac{7}{50}$ **(c)** $18\frac{17}{20} + 21\frac{16}{25} + 20$

10. (a) $17\frac{5}{6} + 19\frac{3}{10}$ **(b)** $13\frac{3}{4} + 15\frac{7}{8} + 10\frac{11}{12}$ **(c)** $8\frac{7}{10} + 6\frac{7}{20} + 8\frac{7}{50}$

11. (a) $\frac{3}{7} - \frac{1}{7}$ **(b)** $\frac{9}{10} - \frac{7}{10}$ **(c)** $\frac{7}{8} - \frac{3}{8}$

12. (a) $\frac{3}{4} - \frac{1}{20}$ **(b)** $\frac{11}{15} - \frac{3}{5}$ **(c)** $\frac{5}{6} - \frac{3}{4}$

13. (a) $3\frac{5}{8} - 2$ **(b)** $11\frac{5}{16} - 7$ **(c)** $20\frac{11}{20} - 9$

14. (a) $7 - \frac{2}{3}$ **(b)** $10 - \frac{5}{9}$ **(c)** $11 - \frac{11}{12}$

15. (a) $8 - 7\frac{2}{5}$ **(b)** $6 - 3\frac{7}{12}$ **(c)** $8 - 5\frac{11}{20}$

16. (a) $3\frac{3}{4} - 1\frac{1}{2}$ **(b)** $5\frac{3}{10} - 2\frac{1}{5}$ **(c)** $11\frac{7}{8} - 10\frac{5}{16}$

17. (a) $5\frac{3}{4} - 2\frac{1}{6}$ **(b)** $8\frac{3}{4} - 6\frac{3}{10}$ **(c)** $5\frac{7}{8} - 4\frac{5}{12}$

18. (a) $4\frac{1}{4} - 3\frac{1}{2}$ **(b)** $5\frac{1}{5} - 2\frac{3}{10}$ **(c)** $6\frac{7}{12} - 4\frac{3}{4}$

19. (a) $8\frac{3}{8} - 5\frac{5}{6}$ **(b)** $7\frac{1}{6} - 4\frac{5}{9}$ **(c)** $11\frac{2}{5} - 9\frac{11}{12}$

20. (a) $14\frac{5}{12} - 11\frac{7}{8}$ **(b)** $15\frac{2}{9} - 7\frac{5}{12}$ **(c)** $20\frac{7}{15} - 19\frac{17}{25}$

21. (a) $\frac{1}{4} + \frac{1}{2} - \frac{1}{8}$ **(b)** $\frac{1}{3} + \frac{1}{6} - \frac{1}{2}$ **(c)** $\frac{1}{2} + \frac{1}{10} - \frac{1}{5}$

22. (a) $\frac{2}{3} + \frac{3}{4} - \frac{5}{6}$ **(b)** $\frac{1}{2} + \frac{2}{3} - \frac{4}{5}$ **(c)** $\frac{1}{2} + \frac{4}{5} - \frac{7}{10}$

23. (a) $7 + \frac{5}{8} - 3$ **(b)** $2\frac{1}{2} + 2 - \frac{7}{12}$ **(c)** $5 + 8\frac{3}{4} - \frac{9}{10}$

24. (a) $2\frac{2}{3} + 2\frac{2}{3} - 5$ **(b)** $4\frac{1}{5} + 1\frac{1}{2} - 3\frac{17}{20}$ **(c)** $5\frac{1}{6} + 2\frac{1}{3} - 1\frac{4}{5}$

25. (a) $10 - 5 + 4\frac{1}{2}$ **(b)** $\frac{1}{2} - \frac{1}{4} + \frac{3}{8}$ **(c)** $\frac{3}{4} - \frac{1}{6} + \frac{5}{12}$

26. (a) $2\frac{5}{6} - 1\frac{3}{4} + \frac{2}{3}$ **(b)** $\frac{2}{3} - \frac{3}{5} + 2\frac{1}{2}$ **(c)** $7\frac{7}{8} - 4\frac{2}{3} + 3\frac{11}{12}$

27. (a) $\frac{1}{4} - \frac{1}{2} + \frac{5}{8}$ **(b)** $\frac{1}{5} - \frac{1}{3} + \frac{2}{15}$ **(c)** $\frac{3}{10} - \frac{7}{15} + \frac{5}{6}$

28. (a) $2 - 2\frac{2}{5} + 1$ **(b)** $3\frac{3}{4} - 4 + 2\frac{1}{2}$ **(c)** $4\frac{3}{8} - 2\frac{2}{3} + 1\frac{5}{12}$

29. (a) $\frac{5}{6} - \frac{1}{3} - \frac{1}{2}$ **(b)** $\frac{11}{12} - \frac{2}{3} - \frac{1}{4}$ **(c)** $\frac{9}{10} - \frac{2}{5} - \frac{1}{3}$

30. (a) $2 - \frac{7}{10} - \frac{1}{2}$ **(b)** $8\frac{1}{5} - 2\frac{2}{3} - 4$ **(c)** $10\frac{1}{8} - 3\frac{5}{6} - 2\frac{3}{4}$

MULTIPLICATION AND DIVISION

1. (a) $\frac{1}{3}$ of 9   (b) $\frac{4}{5}$ of 10   (c) $12 \times \frac{3}{4}$

2. (a) $\frac{7}{8} \times 1$ (b) $0 \times \frac{11}{12}$ (c) $\frac{3}{16} \times 0$

3. (a) $\frac{2}{7} \times 3$ (b) $10 \times \frac{5}{9}$ (c) $6 \times \frac{3}{4}$

4. (a) $\frac{1}{3} \times \frac{1}{3}$ (b) $\frac{1}{3} \times \frac{1}{4}$ (c) $\frac{3}{4}$ of $\frac{3}{4}$

5. (a) $\frac{3}{4}$ of $\frac{4}{5}$ (b) $\frac{5}{6} \times \frac{8}{9}$ (c) $\frac{5}{7} \times \frac{3}{10}$

6. (a) $\frac{2}{3} \times \frac{3}{4}$ (b) $\frac{3}{10}$ of $\frac{5}{6}$ (c) $\frac{2}{9}$ of $\frac{3}{8}$

7. (a) $1\frac{1}{2} \times 3$ (b) $2\frac{5}{6} \times 2$ (c) $4 \times 3\frac{15}{16}$

8. (a) $\frac{3}{4} \times 1\frac{1}{3}$ (b) $\frac{2}{5}$ of $2\frac{1}{2}$ (c) $3\frac{1}{3} \times \frac{1}{3}$

9. (a) $2\frac{1}{4} \times 2\frac{1}{4}$ (b) $1\frac{1}{2} \times 2\frac{1}{4}$ (c) $4\frac{3}{8} \times 1\frac{2}{3}$

10. (a) $2\frac{7}{10} \times 3\frac{8}{9}$ (b) $2\frac{1}{10} \times 1\frac{11}{14}$ (c) $1\frac{13}{50} \times 1\frac{7}{18}$

11. (a) $4 \div 9$ (b) $16 \div 24$ (c) $22 \div 9$

12. (a) $\frac{3}{4} \div 1$ (b) $\frac{2}{3} \div 5$ (c) $2\frac{11}{16} \div 4$

13. (a) $1 \div \frac{1}{5}$ (b) $12 \div \frac{2}{3}$ (c) $21 \div \frac{7}{8}$

14. (a) $\frac{3}{5} \div \frac{3}{5}$ (b) $\frac{1}{2} \div \frac{1}{12}$ (c) $\frac{3}{8} \div \frac{3}{16}$

15. (a) $\frac{2}{5} \div \frac{5}{6}$ (b) $2\frac{7}{10} \div \frac{3}{10}$ (c) $5\frac{5}{6} \div \frac{7}{12}$

16. (a) $\frac{3}{4} \div 1\frac{1}{6}$ (b) $\frac{4}{5} \div 2\frac{2}{3}$ (c) $\frac{17}{20} \div 3\frac{2}{5}$

17. (a) $1 \div 3\frac{1}{2}$ (b) $3 \div 2\frac{3}{4}$ (c) $21 \div 4\frac{2}{3}$

18. (a) $5\frac{2}{3} \div 3\frac{1}{2}$ (b) $12\frac{1}{2} \div 3\frac{3}{4}$ (c) $10\frac{2}{7} \div 1\frac{13}{14}$

19. (a) $2\frac{1}{5} \div 4\frac{1}{8}$ (b) $2\frac{2}{3} \div 3\frac{1}{5}$ (c) $2\frac{7}{10} \div 5\frac{5}{8}$

20. (a) $\dfrac{1\frac{2}{5}}{7}$ (b) $\dfrac{10}{3\frac{1}{3}}$ (c) $\dfrac{5\frac{3}{5}}{2\frac{7}{10}}$

21. (a) $\frac{1}{2} \times \frac{1}{2} \times \frac{1}{2}$ (b) $\frac{1}{3} \times \frac{1}{3} \times \frac{1}{3}$ (c) $\frac{1}{2} \times \frac{1}{3} \times \frac{1}{5}$

22. (a) $\frac{2}{3} \times \frac{3}{4} \times \frac{4}{5}$ (b) $\frac{7}{10} \times \frac{5}{8} \times \frac{4}{7}$ (c) $\frac{5}{12} \times \frac{4}{5} \times \frac{9}{10}$

23. (a) $5 \times \frac{3}{10} \times \frac{1}{6}$ (b) $2\frac{2}{5} \times \frac{7}{8} \times 1\frac{3}{7}$ (c) $\frac{9}{16} \times 2\frac{2}{3} \times 1\frac{1}{3}$

24. (a) $3\frac{3}{4} \times \frac{8}{25} \times 2\frac{1}{2}$ (b) $\frac{7}{11} \times 1 \times 1\frac{4}{7}$ (c) $8\frac{3}{4} \times 1\frac{1}{15} \times 1\frac{1}{4}$

25. (a) $\frac{2}{3} \times \frac{3}{5} \div \frac{8}{15}$ (b) $\frac{3}{4} \times 1\frac{1}{3} \div 2$ (c) $1\frac{7}{8} \times 1\frac{1}{3} \div 2\frac{1}{2}$

26. (a) $(1\frac{1}{8} \div 3) \times 1\frac{3}{5}$ (b) $(\frac{3}{7} \div 3\frac{1}{7}) \times 11$ (c) $(1\frac{7}{10} \div 6\frac{4}{5}) \times 1\frac{1}{3}$

27. $\dfrac{3\frac{1}{3} \times \frac{9}{20}}{3\frac{3}{5}}$ **28.** $\dfrac{7\frac{1}{2}}{5\frac{5}{8} \times 2\frac{2}{9}}$

29. $\dfrac{2\frac{1}{7}}{3\frac{13}{14}} \times 11$ **30.** $8\frac{2}{5} \times \dfrac{3\frac{1}{3}}{5\frac{1}{4}}$

FRACTIONAL QUANTITIES

1. What fraction is 2 of 5?
2. What fraction is 7 of 10?
3. What fraction of 5 is 2?
4. What fraction of 10 is 7?
5. Express 2 as a fraction of 5.
6. Express 7 as a fraction of 10.
7. What fraction of 8 is 6?
8. What fraction is 16 of 24?
9. What fraction is 60 of 100?
10. Express 375 as a fraction of 1000.
11. What fraction of 2 is $1\frac{1}{2}$?
12. What fraction of $4\frac{1}{2}$ is 3?
13. What fraction of $7\frac{1}{2}$ is $2\frac{1}{2}$?
14. What fraction is 1.2 of 4?
15. Express 0.36 as a fraction of 1.8.
16. What fraction of 9 litres is 3 litres?
17. What fraction of £60 is £45?
18. Express 18p as a fraction of 48p.
19. What fraction is 68 kg of 100 kg?
20. What fraction of 300 boys is 180 boys?
21. What fraction of £1 is 20p?
22. Express 1 mm as a fraction of 1 cm.
23. What fraction is 10 min of 1 h?
24. What fraction of 2 tonnes is 100 kg?
25. What fraction of 4 litres is 750 ml?
26. Express 1.1 mm as a fraction of 1.1 cm.
27. Express 45p as a fraction of £2.40.
28. What fraction is 40 s of 3 min?
29. What fraction of 0.5 g is 375 mg?
30. What fraction of $2\frac{1}{2}$ km is 750 m?

PROBLEMS

1. 40 prizes are purchased for use at a party. If 4 prizes are left, what fraction was used?

2. In a class of 30 children, 18 can swim one length of the pool.
   (a) What fraction of the class can swim one length?
   (b) What fraction of the class cannot swim one length?

3. In a firm with 2000 employees, $\frac{4}{5}$ of them work overtime.
   (a) How many work overtime?
   (b) How many do not work overtime?

4. In a full minor league soccer programme of 40 matches, $\frac{7}{10}$ of them were home wins and $\frac{1}{8}$ of them were drawn. How many matches were won by the away team?

5. After spending £1.50, $\frac{7}{10}$ of a sum of money remains. What was the original sum of money?

6. A man is $6\frac{1}{2}$ cm taller than his wife and their son is $4\frac{3}{5}$ cm shorter than his mother. How much taller than his son is the father?

7. $\frac{3}{5}$ of a choir is female. If the number of males is 20, what is the size of the choir?

8. Calculate the area of a square of edge $4\frac{1}{2}$ m.

9. Of the cars in an auction $\frac{1}{3}$ were British and $\frac{1}{4}$ were European. If the others amounted to 50 cars, how many cars were being auctioned?

10. An oil drum is half full. After drawing off 20 litres it is then $\frac{1}{6}$ full. Calculate its capacity.

39

11. Write the following in order of size, largest first: $\frac{13}{15}, \frac{11}{12}, \frac{17}{20}, \frac{5}{6}, \frac{9}{10}$.

12. How many sheets of paper $\frac{7}{500}$ cm thick are in a pile $3\frac{1}{2}$ cm high?

13. A hiker walks $13\frac{1}{2}$ km in $2\frac{1}{4}$ hours. How many kilometres per hour does he walk on average?

14. The hiker in the previous question later walks $20\frac{4}{5}$ km in $3\frac{1}{4}$ hours. What is his average speed for this walk?

15. The profit from a business is shared equally by four directors after $\frac{2}{5}$ is deducted for tax, dividends to shareholders etc. What fraction of the profit does each director receive?

16. In three days $\frac{1}{4}$ of the supply of petrol at a garage is sold and $\frac{1}{2}$ of the remainder in the next three days. What fraction of the original supply is left?

17. A shop window measures $3\frac{1}{5}$ m by $2\frac{1}{4}$ m. What length of beading would be required to fasten round the edges, allowing $\frac{1}{2}$ m for waste?

18. A lady buys $3\frac{3}{5}$ m of material at a total cost of £16.20. What is the price of the material per metre?

19. A man possesses $\frac{5}{8}$ of all shares in a company and later sells $\frac{2}{5}$ of his holding. What fraction of the company shares does he now hold?

20. $\frac{2}{3}$ of the records in a collection were classical music and $\frac{3}{4}$ of the remaining records were traditional jazz. What fraction of the collection comprised other types of music?

Approximation and Estimation

APPROXIMATIONS

Write the following to the nearest 10:

1. (a) 24	**(b)** 38	**(c)** 82
2. (a) 143	**(b)** 569	**(c)** 991
3. (a) 9	**(b)** 3	**(c)** $6\frac{1}{2}$
4. (a) 3487	**(b)** 5212	**(c)** 8053

Write the following to the nearest 100:

5. (a) 342	**(b)** 576	**(c)** 810
6. (a) 1856	**(b)** 4244	**(c)** 7092
7. (a) 78	**(b)** 43	**(c)** 95.5
8. (a) 24059	**(b)** 30270	**(c)** 67134

Write the following to the nearest 50:

9. (a) 76	**(b)** 74	**(c)** 25.5
10. (a) 284	**(b)** 317	**(c)** 936

Write the following to the nearest 500:

11. (a) 700	**(b)** 800	**(c)** 200
12. (a) 1880	**(b)** 6345	**(c)** 8050

Write the following to the nearest 1000:

13. (a) 3200	**(b)** 7600	**(c)** 9279
14. (a) 14286	**(b)** 751	**(c)** 19597

Write the following to the nearest 10000:

15. (a) 28500	**(b)** 63482	**(c)** 7219
16. (a) 153280	**(b)** 228709	**(c)** 806000

Write the following to the nearest 100000:

17. (a) 173000	**(b)** 328255	**(c)** 876500
18. (a) 79024	**(b)** 117243	**(c)** 965000

Write the following to the nearest 1000000:

19. (a) 1600000	**(b)** 3400000	**(c)** 9700000
20. (a) 26375000	**(b)** 35550000	**(c)** 99600000

Write the following to the nearest whole number:

21. (a) 7.2   **(b)** 8.9   **(c)** $1\frac{1}{3}$

22. (a) 0.6   **(b)** $\frac{3}{5}$ **(c)** $\frac{1}{4}$

23. (a) 27.6   **(b)** $15\frac{3}{5}$ **(c)** $98\frac{1}{4}$

24. (a) 1.58   **(b)** 0.04   **(c)** 0.625

Write the following to the nearest tenth:

25. (a) 0.72   **(b)** 1.28   **(c)** 10.64

26. (a) 0.07   **(b)** 8.04   **(c)** 13.065

Write the following to the nearest hundredth:

27. (a) 1.073   **(b)** 2.456   **(c)** 12.582

28. (a) 0.009   **(b)** 2.013   **(c)** 27.099

Consider, but do not fully evaluate, the following calculations and from the possible answers which appear in brackets, select the most appropriate:

29. $17.026 + 23$ (17.05, 40, 6, 17.25)

30. $5 - 2.99$ (3, 1, 2, 8)

31. 3.014×7.01 (21, 10, 32, 4)

32. $15 \div 4.929$ (10, 60, 4, 3)

33. $3\frac{49}{50} + 7\frac{1}{100}$ (10, 21, $\frac{4}{7}$, 11)

34. $16 - \frac{99}{100}$ (15, 16, 17, 0)

35. $5\frac{19}{20} \times 3\frac{1}{20}$ (24, 18, 8, 2)

36. $\frac{11}{20} \div \frac{25}{99}$ ($\frac{1}{2}$, $\frac{1}{4}$, 2, 4)

37. $12.02 - 3.98 + 4$ (20, 4, 5, 12)

38. $34.995 - 17 - 17.001$ (1, 0, 35, 34)

39. $\dfrac{4.01 \times 3.008}{2.99}$ (6, 5, 4, 3)

40. $\dfrac{100.01}{37 - 11.99}$ (2, 1, 52, 4)

ESTIMATIONS

Select from the alternatives in brackets the one you estimate will most accurately complete the statement:

1. The height of a man is (3.1 m, 1.75 m, 102 cm, 5 m)

2. The capacity of a teacup is (1 litre, 20 ml, 200 ml, 1500 ml)

3. A paper-clip weighs (0.25 g, 25 g, 0.025 g, 250 g)

4. The diameter of a 10p coin is (28 mm, 5 cm, 1 cm, 48 mm)

5. The area of a gentleman's pocket handkerchief is (1 km², 30.25 cm², 1600 cm², 1 m²)

6. The mass of an apple is (125 kg, 12.5 kg, 125 mg, 125 g)

7. The volume of a sugar cube is (1 m³, 1 cm³, 1 mm³, 27 mm³)

8. A household bucket holds (20 litres, 1 litre, 2 litres, 9 litres)

9. The mass of an elephant is (1 tonne, 7 tonnes, 24 tonnes, 56 tonnes)

10. The length of a double-decker bus is (200 cm, 3000 mm, 8 m, 25 m)

11. The width of a cricket bat is (1 m, 2 cm, 10 cm, 10 mm)

12. The attendance at a Wembley F.A. Cup Final is (1 000 000, 100 000, 10 000, 1000)

13. The time it takes to write the name 'Charles Dickens' is (50 s, 1.5 s, 8 s, 1.5 min)

14. The mass of a sack of household coal is (5 kg, 5 tonnes, 500 kg, 50 kg)

15. The length of a spectacle case is (16 cm, 1.6 m, 16 m, 0.16 km)

16. A top-class sprinter in 10 seconds can run (100 m, 500 m, 1 km, $1\frac{1}{2}$ km)

17. The thickness of a hair is (0.5 cm, 3 mm, 0.35 cm, 0.2 mm)

18. The length of an airport runway is (100 m, 20 km, 10 000 m, 3 km)

19. The area of the surface of a table-tennis table is (24 m², 10 m², 4 m², 1 m²)

20. The volume of a classroom is (150 m³, 150 cm³, 1 km³, 0.5 km³)

Averages

MISCELLANEOUS PROBLEMS

1. A child saves in 4 weeks 85p, £1.10, £1.42 and 95p. What is the average amount saved per week?

2. Three schools in a town raised money in aid of cancer research. What was the average amount raised by each school if the individual school totals were £750.35, £920.70 and £1002.55?

3. During one year the amount of rain which fell in a district averaged 2.34 cm per month. What was the total rainfall for the whole year?

4. The times, to the nearest minute, a person had to wait for a bus on 5 weekdays were 1 min, 12 min, 6 min, 2 min and 8 min. Calculate the average waiting time to the nearest minute.

5. Successive novels written by an author have 218, 195, 228, 187, 206 and 214 pages respectively. Calculate the average number of pages in each book.

6. The average mass of four parcels is 10 kg. If three of them weigh 7 kg, 9 kg, and 15 kg respectively, what is the mass of the fourth parcel?

7. A matchbox displays average contents to be 87 matches. How many matches could be expected in 200 boxes?

8. Two beakers each contain 350 ml of mercury and two others each contain 250 ml of mercury. What average amount does each beaker hold?

9. If the average of a set of numbers is 4 and the total is 24, how many numbers are there in the set?

10. A racing driver completed 4 laps of a track with lap times of 2.12 min, 2.08 min, 2.15 min and 2.17 min. What was his average lap time?

11. A firm employs 3 grades of worker, the average basic wage being £78 per week. A first-grade worker receives £91 per week, while a second-grade worker receives £74 per week. What is the basic wage of a worker in the third grade?

12. Church collections at 10 consecutive Sunday morning services were £8.40, £12.25, £12, £8.05, £12.20, £8.50, £8.10, £8.50, £13.25 and £8.75. What was the average morning collection?

13. The average of two numbers is 3. If one of the numbers is $2\frac{1}{4}$ what is the other?

14. In a springboard diving competition a diver gains 92.03, 105.92, 81.8, 98.45 and 99.1 points in his series of dives. Calculate the average number of points per dive.

15. Five numbers have an average of 42. If the average of the first 3 numbers is 38, what is the average of the other 2 numbers?

16. Four oarsmen weigh 77.5 kg, 75 kg, 75.2 kg and 74.8 kg respectively. What is the average mass of an oarsman?

17. The average mass of three suitcases is 15 kg. If the average mass of two of them is 16 kg, what is the mass of the third?

18. The total of four numbers is 32. If the average of two of them is 7, what is the average of the other two?

19. The average sale of a magazine for each of the first three months of a year was 43 025 copies, while the average for each of the next three months was 37 507 copies. How many copies were sold during the six months?

20. The marks gained by 30 police cadets in an initiative test were as follows: 1 cadet gained 4 marks, 3 gained 5 marks, 2 gained 6 marks, 7 gained 7 marks, 11 gained 8 marks and 6 gained 9 marks. Calculate the average mark.

Percentages

EQUIVALENCE

In the table below one way of writing a fraction has been filled in and you have to fill in the other two columns with an equivalent amount. Make sure that the first column is written in lowest terms.

	vulgar fractions	decimal fractions	percentages
1.	$\frac{1}{2}$		
2.		0.1	
3.			20 %
4.	$\frac{1}{4}$		
5.		0.05	
6.			40 %
7.	$\frac{3}{10}$		
8.		0.15	
9.			60 %
10.	$\frac{3}{4}$		
11.		0.7	
12.			35 %
13.	$\frac{9}{20}$		
14.		0.8	
15.			85 %
16.	$\frac{9}{10}$		
17.		0.65	
18.			100 %
19.	$\frac{1}{100}$		
20.		2	

MISCELLANEOUS

1. What is 50 % of 100?
2. What is 50 % of 300?
3. What is 50 % of 150?
4. What is 50 % of 20?
5. What is 25 % of 100?
6. What is 25 % of 700?
7. What is 75 % of 120 kg?
8. What is 75 % of £16?
9. What is 10 % of 15 m?
10. What is 20 % of 20 litres?
11. What is 5 % of 1 min?
12. What is 15 % of 80p?
13. What is 30 % of £1?
14. What is 40 % of £2?
15. What is 60 % of 25 tonnes?
16. What is 80 % of 1000 ml?
17. What is $12\frac{1}{2}$ % of 16?
18. What is $2\frac{1}{2}$ % of £80?
19. What is 125 % of 500?
20. What is $33\frac{1}{3}$ % of 240?
21. Express 5 as a percentage of 10
22. Express 6 as a percentage of 8
23. Express 3 as a percentage of 12
24. Express 4 as a percentage of 20
25. Express 10 as a percentage of 25
26. Express 18 as a percentage of 30
27. Express 24 as a percentage of 80
28. Express 28 as a percentage of 40
29. Express 8 as a percentage of 4
30. Express 15 as a percentage of 5
31. Increase 16 by 50 %
32. Increase 50 by 10 %
33. Increase 100 km by 25 %
34. Increase 240 kg by 75 %
35. Increase 32 litres by 200 %
36. Decrease 25 g by 20 %
37. Decrease 70 by 30 %
38. Decrease £280 by 5 %
39. Decrease 5 tonnes by 70 %
40. Decrease 75 by 100 %

PROBLEMS

1. On receiving a consignment of eggs a grocer finds that 2 % are broken. What percentage are not broken?

2. Of the cars produced in a factory, 22 % were red, 26 % yellow, 16 % white and 18 % blue. What percentage were other colours?

3. In one particular week the attendance at a holiday camp showed that 8 % were between 1 and 5 years of age, 20 % between 6 and 15 years, 15 % between 16 and 25 years and 35 % between 26 and 40 years. What percentage were over 40 years of age?

4. What was the percentage score of a boy who scored 17 out of 20 in a test?

5. A soldier scored 19 out of 25 on the shooting-range. What was his percentage score?

6. Write down the following in order of size, largest first: $\frac{1}{2}$, 45 %, 0.51.

7. In a school of 750 pupils, 20 % leave the premises at lunch-time. How many pupils do not stay at school during this period?

8. In a works employing 1250 people, 70 % stay for a canteen lunch. How many people have lunch elsewhere?

9. A worker on a basic wage of £75 per week received a 10 % pay rise. What was his new weekly wage?

10. A machine produced 1350 articles during an eight-hour shift. If its efficiency was improved by 20 %, how many articles would it now produce during a shift?

11. A dress costing £35 was reduced in a sale by 10 %. What was the sale price?

12. In a school library there were 3500 books. If 52 % were fiction, 34 % were non-fiction and the remainder were reference, how many reference books did the library possess?

13. A jeweller bought a ring for £50 and sold it, making a profit of 30 %. At what price did he sell it?

14. A second-hand dealer bought a chair for £5 and later sold it at a loss of 20 %. At what price did he sell?

15. If a coffee-table can be produced for £20 and is sold for £30, what percentage profit is made?

16. A used car was bought for £1000 and a year later sold for £800. What percentage loss did this represent?

17. The interest rate in a building society was $8\frac{1}{2}$ % per annum. If a man had invested £650, what would the interest be at the end of a year?

18. Write down the following in order of size, smallest first: 0.802, $\frac{17}{20}$, 79 %, 0.785, $\frac{4}{5}$.

19. A pair of shoes had been reduced in a sale by 10 % and the sale price was £18. What was the price before the sale?

20. If an investment grows by 10 % per annum, what would £100 amount to after 2 years?

Speed

MISCELLANEOUS QUESTIONS

$$\text{Distance} = \text{average speed} \times \text{time}$$

Complete the following table.

	average speed (km/h)	time (h)	distance (km)
1.	40	5	
2.	28	6	
3.	880	1.6	
4.	2800	0.2	
5.	160	$\frac{3}{4}$	
6.	25		100
7.	48		240
8.	12.5		20
9.	$6\frac{1}{2}$		39
10.		3	126
11.		5	4530
12.		3.6	18
13.		0.75	360
14.		$\frac{7}{10}$	112
15.		$4\frac{3}{4}$	76

16. What length of time should be allowed for a journey of 280 km if an average speed of 56 km/h can be maintained?

17. How far will an aircraft travel in $4\frac{1}{2}$ hours at an average speed of 740 km/h?

18. A cyclist covers 105 km in $3\frac{3}{4}$ h. Work out his average speed.

19. A train maintains a speed of 165 km/h for 18 min. How far does it travel in this time?

20. A spaceship travels 3852 km in 0.5 h. What is its average speed over this distance?

21. Change 40 km/h to m/h.

22. Change 60 km/h to m/min.

23. Change 270 km/h to m/s.

24. Change 81 km/h to m/s.

25. Convert 18 m/s to m/min.

26. Convert 8.5 m/s to m/h.

27. Convert 50 m/s to km/h.

28. Convert $12\frac{1}{2}$ m/s to km/h.

29. Change 4.2 cm/s to cm/min.

30. Change $1\frac{1}{4}$ cm/s to m/min.

31. Change 15.3 m/min to cm/min.

32. Change $2\frac{2}{5}$ m/min to cm/s.

33. A helicopter is travelling at a speed of 126 km/h. What is the equivalent speed in m/s?

34. An athlete runs the 100 metres in 10 seconds. Work out his average speed for the race in km/h.

35. Tape is fed through a machine at a rate of 1.5 cm/s. What is the equivalent rate in m/h?

36. Two trains are travelling towards each other at speeds of 65 km/h and 90 km/h. What is the speed at which they are approaching each other?

37. Two trains 86 km apart are travelling towards each other at speeds of 104 km/h and 68 km/h. How long will they take to meet?

38. A goods train travelling at 57 km/h is overtaken by an express travelling at 113 km/h on an adjacent line. How far ahead of the goods train is the express after 1 hour?

39. In the previous question how long will it take for the express to be 42 km ahead of the goods train?

40. A car travelling at 72 km/h passes over a motorway viaduct in 11 seconds. Work out the length of the bridge in metres.

Ratio and Proportion

RATIO

Express the following ratios in their simplest form:

1. (a) $2:2$	(b) $5:5$	(c) $5:10$
2. (a) $8:4$	(b) $2:6$	(c) $3:12$
3. (a) $20:4$	(b) $6:42$	(c) £50:£5
4. (a) $4:6$	(b) $8:6$	(c) $8:10$
5. (a) $9:15$	(b) $15\,g:6\,g$	(c) $15:20$
6. (a) $30:20$	(b) $40:60$	(c) $40:30$
7. (a) $14:8$	(b) $49:42$	(c) $56:64$
8. (a) $24:30$	(b) $35:25$	(c) $36:27$
9. (a) $50:50$	(b) $25\,m:50\,m$	(c) $90:30$
10. (a) $60:80$	(b) $60:45$	(c) $50:75$
11. (a) $100:100$	(b) $100:60$	(c) $75:100$
12. (a) $100:500$	(b) $250:1000$	(c) $900:300$
13. (a) $120:90$	(b) $150:200$	(c) $800:1000$
14. (a) $2:4:6$	(b) $40:25:10$	(c) $30:120:150$
15. (a) $1\,mm:1\,cm$	(b) $1\,h:30\,min$	(c) $1\,week:3\,days$
16. (a) £3:£4.50	(b) £1:35p	(c) $2\,kg:500\,g$
17. (a) $\frac{1}{2}:\frac{1}{2}$	(b) $\frac{1}{4}:\frac{3}{4}$	(c) $\frac{1}{2}:1$
18. (a) $\frac{3}{8}:\frac{3}{4}$	(b) $2:1\frac{1}{2}$	(c) $\frac{2}{3}:\frac{1}{2}$
19. (a) $0.5:1$	(b) $1.2:0.3$	(c) $4:0.8$
20. (a) $2.5:3.5$	(b) $3:0.25$	(c) $0.35:0.4$

Supply the missing value in each of the following:

21. $4:4 = 8:$ **22.** $\ :4 = 3:1$

23. $2:10 = \quad :20$ **24.** $2:\quad = 5:50$

25. $4:\quad = 2:3$ **26.** $6:\quad = 3:4$

27. $8:10 = 4:$ **28.** $10:\quad = 20:30$

29. $\dfrac{}{15} = \dfrac{4}{5}$ **30.** $\dfrac{5}{6} = \dfrac{}{30}$

DIRECT PROPORTION

1. Five records cost £15. What will be the cost of (a) 1 record,
   (b) 7 records, (c) 15 records?

2. A car uses 4 litres of petrol in travelling 52 km.
   (a) How far will it travel on 8 litres of petrol?
   (b) How far will it travel on 20 litres of petrol?
   (c) How much petrol will it require for a journey of 78 km?

3. An examiner marks scripts at an average rate of 9 scripts per hour.
   How long will it take him to mark a quota of (a) 360 scripts,
   (b) 540 scripts?

4. Four textbooks cost £3.
   (a) How much will 40 textbooks cost?
   (b) How many books can be purchased for £48?

5. 25 screws weigh 200 g.
   (a) Calculate the mass of 5 screws.
   (b) Calculate the mass of 100 screws.
   (c) How many screws are needed to weigh 1 kg?

6. After 14 matches a footballer has scored 9 goals. How many will
   he score in a full season of 42 matches if he maintains this rate of
   scoring?

7. A catering firm allows 5 cakes for every 4 persons attending a
   function. How many cakes will they provide if the attendance is
   to be (a) 60 persons, (b) 200 persons?

8. Eight loaves weigh 7 kg.
   (a) What is the mass of two dozen loaves?
   (b) How many loaves are needed to weigh 35 kg?

9. A club secretary can address 5 envelopes in 2 minutes. How many
   minutes will it take him to address envelopes for all 360 club
   members?

10. When the rates in a district are 80p in the pound, the amount
    payable on a property is £128. What will be the amount payable if
    the rate is increased to 85p in the pound?

INVERSE PROPORTION

1. A tank of oil can empty in 16 minutes if 1 outlet valve is fully open. How long will it take to empty if 2 outlet valves are fully open?

2. A housewife has sufficient coal to last 12 days providing she uses only 2 buckets of coal a day. How long will the coal last if she uses **(a)** 1 bucket a day, **(b)** 3 buckets a day, **(c)** 4 buckets a day?

3. A lorry can transport a supply of building materials in 4 hours, making 3 journeys each hour. If 4 journeys could be made each hour, how long would the job take?

4. A journey can be completed in 3 hours if an average speed of 68 km/h is maintained. How long will the journey take at an average speed of 51 km/h?

5. A man can save the train fare for his holiday in 20 weeks if he saves £1.20 per week. If he wishes to save up the fare in 16 weeks how much per week must he save?

6. A building contractor estimates that 6 men can complete a job in 8 days. How long would the same job take 8 men?

7. A sports council sponsors 24 athletes for special coaching at £70 per athlete. How many athletes could be sponsored for the same amount of money if the fees were £80 per athlete?

8. A farmer has sufficient fodder to feed his herd of 64 cows for 15 days.
(a) How long would this amount of food last a herd of 80 cows?
(b) How many cows would be in the herd if the food were to last 20 days?

9. 80 books each 2.5 cm fit exactly on a shelf. How many books would fit on the shelf if they were **(a)** 1 cm wide, **(b)** 2 cm wide, **(c)** 4 cm wide?

10. A train travelling at an average speed of 96 km/h completes a journey in $4\frac{1}{2}$ hours. How long would the same journey take a car at an average speed of 72 km/h?

MISCELLANEOUS PROBLEMS

1. 3 kg of potatoes cost 63p. What will be the cost of **(a)** 6 kg, **(b)** 4 kg, **(c)** 30 kg?

2. 0.5 litres of motor oil cost 43p. Calculate the cost of **(a)** 1 litre, **(b)** 5 litres, **(c)** 12 litres.

3. A warehouse is sufficiently high to stack 15 boxes each 60 cm deep. How many boxes 45 cm deep would form a stack of the same height?

4. Two squares have edges of 2 m and 4 m respectively. What is the ratio of their areas expressed in the simplest form?

5. A car is bought for £4900 and later sold at a loss of £700. What is the ratio of the selling price to the buying price expressed in the simplest terms?

6. A machine produces 125 articles in 20 minutes.
(a) How many articles will it produce in 1 hour?
(b) How many minutes will it take to produce 1000 articles?

7. A man earns £11 for 4 hours' work. At this rate how much will he earn in **(a)** 1 hour, **(b)** 3 hours?
How long will it take him to earn **(c)** £16.50, **(d)** £44?

8. A cyclist completes a journey in $3\frac{1}{2}$ hours at an average speed of 24 km/h. How long would the journey take by car at an average speed of 56 km/h?

9. An aircraft is travelling at a steady speed of 480 km/h. How far will it travel in **(a)** 30 min, **(b)** 40 min, **(c)** 55 min?

10. 480 sheets of paper have a total thickness of 4 cm. What is the thickness of **(a)** 240 sheets, **(b)** 600 sheets?
How many sheets would be in a pile **(c)** 3 cm thick, **(d)** $1\frac{1}{2}$ cm thick?

Binary Number

CONVERSION

Write the following binary numbers in denary:

1. (a) 1   (b) 10
2. (a) 11   (b) 100
3. (a) 101   (b) 110
4. (a) 111   (b) 1000
5. (a) 1101   (b) 10110
6. (a) 11000   (b) 11010
7. (a) 11011   (b) 100000
8. (a) 100110   (b) 101010
9. (a) 110001   (b) 110011
10. (a) 111000   (b) 111010
11. (a) 1111001   (b) 111111
12. (a) 1000000   (b) 1000101
13. (a) 1001011   (b) 1010110
14. (a) 1101010   (b) 1110101
15. (a) 1111011   (b) 11111111

Write the following denary numbers in binary:

16. (a) 9   (b) 10
17. (a) 17   (b) 21
18. (a) 25   (b) 29
19. (a) 35   (b) 45
20. (a) 50   (b) 57
21. (a) 68   (b) 74
22. (a) 89   (b) 100
23. (a) 147   (b) 160
24. (a) 200   (b) 220
25. (a) 270   (b) 294
26. (a) 300   (b) 350
27. (a) 400   (b) 450
28. (a) 512   (b) 513
29. (a) 700   (b) 800
30. (a) 900   (b) 1000

ADDITION AND SUBTRACTION

All questions and answers are in binary notation.

1. (a) $\begin{array}{r} 1 \\ +\ 1 \\ \hline \end{array}$
  (b) $\begin{array}{r} 11 \\ +\ 1 \\ \hline \end{array}$
  (c) $\begin{array}{r} 10 \\ +\ 10 \\ \hline \end{array}$

2. (a) $\begin{array}{r} 11 \\ +\ 10 \\ \hline \end{array}$
  (b) $\begin{array}{r} 11 \\ +\ 11 \\ \hline \end{array}$
  (c) $\begin{array}{r} 11 \\ +\ 101 \\ \hline \end{array}$

3. (a) $\begin{array}{r} 1001 \\ +\ 111 \\ \hline \end{array}$
  (b) $\begin{array}{r} 1010 \\ +\ 1110 \\ \hline \end{array}$
  (c) $\begin{array}{r} 11011 \\ +\ 1001 \\ \hline \end{array}$

4. (a) 101 + 101010 + 10110
  (b) 1110 + 10101 + 101101 + 1001
  (c) 1101101 + 11011 + 111101 + 100

5. (a) Add 1011, 101101, 1110111 and 1001001
  (b) Find the sum of 10101010, 1110101, 1101 and 10111
  (c) Find the total of 101100110, 111, 10101 and 1010110

6. (a) $\begin{array}{r} 11 \\ -\ 10 \\ \hline \end{array}$
  (b) $\begin{array}{r} 100 \\ -\ 11 \\ \hline \end{array}$
  (c) $\begin{array}{r} 101 \\ -\ 10 \\ \hline \end{array}$

7. (a) $\begin{array}{r} 1000 \\ -\ 111 \\ \hline \end{array}$
  (b) $\begin{array}{r} 1010 \\ -\ 101 \\ \hline \end{array}$
  (c) $\begin{array}{r} 1111 \\ -\ 1001 \\ \hline \end{array}$

8. (a) $\begin{array}{r} 10010 \\ -\ 1001 \\ \hline \end{array}$
  (b) $\begin{array}{r} 11011 \\ -\ 1101 \\ \hline \end{array}$
  (c) $\begin{array}{r} 101101 \\ -\ 10111 \\ \hline \end{array}$

9. (a) 1101011 − 110101
  (b) 1001000 − 111111
  (c) 1111001 − 1000110

10. (a) From 10000000 subtract 1010111
  (b) Subtract 1111011 from 10110110
  (c) How much greater is 101101101 than 10110111?

MULTIPLICATION AND DIVISION

All questions and answers are in binary notation.

1. **(a)** 11
    × 10

  (b) 101
    × 10

  (c) 110
    × 11

2. **(a)** 1010
    × 100

  (b) 1100
    × 101

  (c) 1101
    × 111

3. **(a)** 10101
    × 11

  (b) 11010
    × 101

  (c) 11100
    × 111

4. **(a)** 100110
    × 11

  (b) 101111
    × 101

  (c) 110100
    × 110

5. **(a)** Multiply 1010 by 1010
  (b) 10111 times 1101
  (c) Find the product of 101011 and 1110

6. **(a)** 100 ÷ 10   **(b)** 1000 ÷ 10   **(c)** 1100 ÷ 10

7. **(a)** $\frac{1001}{11}$ **(b)** $\frac{1111}{11}$ **(c)** $\frac{10010}{11}$

8. **(a)** $\frac{10000}{100}$ **(b)** $\frac{11100}{100}$ **(c)** $\frac{100100}{100}$

9. **(a)** $\frac{10100}{101}$ **(b)** $\frac{100011}{101}$ **(c)** $\frac{110010}{101}$

10. **(a)** Divide 110000 by 110

   (b) Divide 1001000 by 1000

   (c) Divide 1100100 by 1010